JOURNEYS OF THE HUMAN HEART

With best wishes—

[signature]

for Bud Meyers
and Ruth Farrell

Also by the author
The Morning People
An American Romantic

Second Printing

PRELUDE

When the tide of love
comes to you,
it will dress your life
with treasures—
plain and precious:
bits of glass,
as well as diamonds;
ivory
and simple bone.
And each of these
will seem
equally miraculous;
for until that time
you knew only
sand.

Robert Sexton

There are moments in our lives when the world seems to take on a sudden and certain glow. We find ourselves in the midst of an experience or an atmosphere that touches us deeply, and we are moved away from the realm of our ordinary concerns and transported to a place just outside of them: a place of quiet, shimmering magic. We pause, transfixed, as our senses open; and it occurs to us that we have seldom felt so fully alive. We do not know why or how this moment has come; we do not question its beauty. In the midst of its wonder, all that is certain is that we want to hold it, to extend it, and, above all, to share it.

Recently, I spent an entire day filled with such moments. But I was alone, and the longing I felt to share them with someone was left to dangle on the wind, like the silver thread a spider might spin, if he tried to catch a star. And—in that yearning—the glow of the moment dimmed a bit, and some of its magic was sifted away.

But, if you had been there, this is what we might have shared.

JOURNEYS
OF THE HUMAN HEART

ROBERT SEXTON

It is raining in San Francisco.

The clock on the tower of the Ferry Building tells that it is early afternoon, but the sky would not indicate any particular time of day. An unbroken layer of thick, gray clouds stretches for as far as the eye can see, and what little light comes through could belong to dawn as well as dusk.

The city itself rises into these clouds behind silver sheets of rain. Its lights are circled with misty halos, and its voice is hushed. Few people are on its streets, but those who have braved the elements scurry along beneath umbrellas or newspapers, their eyes downcast, measuring the depth of the puddles before them. Yellow taxis, their color somehow more vivid in this light, weave from block to block, heaving plumes of water to the sidewalks, and the curses of soggy pedestrians mark their way. In the tall buildings above, office workers go about their business, every so often glancing from wristwatch to window, wondering if it will clear before rush-hour, and punctuating their wonder with sighs of resignation.

But I am free today. I've done the work I had to do, and no sense of obligation compels me to remain at my desk. Good sense might dictate that I stay at home and clean out that closet or scrub that floor. But I neither hear nor heed its command.

Instead, I have chosen to go into the city and take the ferry to Sausalito. In any weather this is one of my favorite things to do. The voyage across the Bay is a short one, only a half-hour in length, but it puts me at some distance from my everyday patterns and allows me to view my life from a different perspective.

Boarding the ferry, I go to the bar for a cup of coffee. Then, I return to the deck and stand at the rail, sheltered from the rain only by the overhang above.

There are few other passengers at this hour, but those who have come aboard sit in clusters within the lounge. It will not be long before the warmth of the air they breathe clouds the inner surface of the windows. Glancing back, I note that already their forms have grown hazy, like the outlines of people one might see in a dream.

Slowly the ferry begins to move away from its berth. I sip my coffee and settle against the rail and scan the shining scene before me. On my right side San Francisco is a glowing blur, joined to the Bay by the quickening rain. Straight ahead and far away, the Bay Bridge stretches its delicate filaments against the pewter sky. And, still further away, on my left lies the city of Oakland, where I have made my home. And, looking toward it, I first see you.

You stand beneath the overhang on the far side of the deck, peering out at the gulls that inevitably follow the ferry. I can only see your profile, but you seem deeply lost in thought. I wonder for a moment if you are a tourist, for locals never seem to notice the gulls.

A sudden gust of wind drives the rain under the overhang that had sheltered you, and you turn away from the wetness and cross the deck and stand nearer to me.

I sip my coffee and look back toward the city, for I've carried some of the shyness I knew so intensely as a child into my adult years. And, perhaps, you have a trace of it, too, for you did not seem to notice me.

And so we stand together, separated by a few feet of cool, damp air: two strangers on a small ship, peering out at the same scene; silent; sifting through our own thoughts; safe within our shells.

And, thus, we remain, as the ferry churns its way further out upon the Bay, trailed by its escort of gulls. We are like a million other strangers on ten-thousand other ships on a hundred other seas, all across the length and breadth of time. Closed within ourselves, we cope with that which is familiar. We take no risks; we wager nothing. And, even as we know that a smile or a simple hello would put us both at greater ease, we withold even that.

The ferry passes Alcatraz, and even that monumental conversation-piece does not stir us from our solace. As we move nearer to the Pacific, the air grows colder, and we draw our coats more closely around us, that none of our warmth might be lost on the wind.

Raindrops dance on the deck before us, and—far away—San Francisco is now a pale line between the cobalt Bay and sky.

The cup in my hand is empty, but I do not discard it. It is something to hold. From the corner of my eye, I can see that your arms are crossed before you, and I begin to feel a sense of regret. I wish I had said something sooner. But now it is too late. We are only a few minutes away from Sausalito, and our silence has run too long to break. Like a veil of isolation, it hangs awkwardly between us, and its color is the hue of the Bay and the sky. It has been established; we gave it our unspoken consent. No belated word, etched in pale regret, can remove it now.

*But then **this** happens:*

Suddenly, off to our right, on the port side of the ship, a strange whiteness envelopes everything. I look down at the water, and its glare pierces my eyes, and I turn away, blinking, until my eyes adjust. I lift my hand to shield them and turn back to the right to see what this sudden brightness might be.

And you, too, cover your eyes and step to the rail.

And, as the rain pours down around us, we are drawn like moths to a lantern's glow, and we look out at the Bay, then to the far horizon, and then slowly, cautiously, to the source of this brightness—this numbing light—and we raise our faces to the heavens above.

Through a crack in the clouds over the Golden Gate Bridge, the sun has broken upon the earth. One beam falls, and then another, and then another, until a dozen shafts of pure white light line the sky, shattering the grayness of the day.

One beam falls to the hills of Marin, and they become green and yellow, as they are in the spring. Another falls on the Avenues in San Francisco, turning the houses there as white as they truly are. Another brightens the Bridge itself, and once again it acquires grace and beauty, shining like the work of genius that it is. And others rush out to the Pacific, and others to the left and right; but none are so bright as those that reach to us, here upon the Bay.

And, though the rain still falls, the air acquires a sudden warmth that swirls around us, unfolding us. I feel it rush across my face and upon my neck, and my shoulders drop, as the tension within them is eased away. I place my hands on the rail and turn fully to the sun.

And you are there beside me, silent still. But I need not look at your face to know that peace has also come to you; for I have seen your hands upon the rail, and they are open in gentle repose.

For one long moment we are voyagers within a glistening universe, for we have become elemental. The light that falls upon us shimmers, too, upon the water; fills the air; rises through the clouds, into the heavens; and shines through all infinity. It makes us One with all that is. It joins us with our source.

Then—even as the clouds begin to close again, and the scattered rays are narrowed and drawn away—we remain open; soaring; motionless: like gulls that glide upon the wind.

For something, indeed, has happened. Though I can give it no name, it has changed us; and we are not quite the same people we were just a few, short minutes ago. It is as if some added dimension had been given to our vision; as if the sense itself had fully expanded and parted from our power of reason, creating a channel through which light might pass and touch our souls.

The ferry turns upon the water, and a gust of wind splatters us with rain. We move beneath the overhang and again stand alone upon the deck.

Surprising myself, I say to you:

"I'm glad you were here to see that, too."

You nod and smile, and we begin to talk. Awkward and hesitant, perhaps, at first; but then the words begin to flow. You're from there; I'm from here. You wonder when the storm will clear. We say our names and give our hands. Then, much too soon, the ferry lands at Sausalito.

The other passengers hurry off, but we linger there upon the deck, not really certain what to do.

Sausalito is muted in the rain, like a flower that only blooms in sun. Its charms and colors run together; its beauty, sleeping through this weather.

Finally, I think to say:

"I know a place. A small cafe. If you would like . . ."

And yes; you would. "A cup of coffee would be good."

We cross the ramp and leave the ferry and run across the lot to Bridgeway.

The cool rain beats against our brows and mats our hair, and both of us, umbrellaless, remain close to the buildings along the way.

It isn't far. The cafe glows just ahead. Then, in its foyer we pause to reassemble what the rain has undone. And, as we do, the hulking ferry turns on the Bay and begins its voyage back to San Francisco.

We watch it go. Then, we enter the warmth of the cafe. The waiter greets us with a welcome smile, for we are his only customers. The storm has kept the others away.

We sit at a table beside the window and order coffee; and, when the waiter goes, we begin to talk. And whatever opened between us on the ferry remains unlocked, for we speak, not as strangers who have only just met, but as fellow travellers upon this earth: unafraid; unguarded; of substance and worth.

Over coffee, we tell of what we have seen; of what we are now and what we have been. Of faith and joy and moments of fear; of time and of memory; of there and of here. Of those we have loved and those we have lost; of caring too much and counting the cost. Of caring too little when caring was right; of years made of summer; of seasons of night. Of triumphs and trials; of laughter and tears: the span and the measure of all of our years.

And when you ask what I believe, I keep no card within my sleeve; but pause to search the soul I bear, to find the words with which to share that which I hold most dear and true; that which remains always new.

And these are the thoughts I give to you:

I believe that each day of our lives is a journey. We know where it begins, but we cannot know where it will end. All that we have to guide us through the hours and the distance of our travels is the attitude with which we begin.

If we are open to the world; if we approach it with a sense of wonder and eager curiosity; if our intent is to learn and to grow, rather than to merely accumulate still more material rewards, then we will travel unburdened and free. We will move beyond the arenas of competitive endeavor and into the open fields of individual human experience. And, at the end of the day, the journey will have left us with a reserve of both gladness and purpose; and these will linger through the night and give us hope in the coming dawn.

If, however, we begin our journey afflicted by an attitude of cynicism, envy, fear or greed, then the day can bring nothing but self-doubt, frustration and pervasive disenchantment. Burdened by such baggage, we move neither far nor well; and all our possibilities are diminished. And when night falls, and we look back upon the day, resentment and exhaustion are all that remain.

Each journey begins with the first step. But the attitude we bring to that step is the force that will determine its direction, its joy and its value.

I am the second of my parents' four children. I was born on a snowy March night, and I nearly died at birth, due to complications with the delivery and the limits of medicine at that time.

I do not know whether or not this is the reason that I have always felt grateful to be alive, but my earliest memories are of my own fascination with the fact of life itself. In my mind's eye I can still see the child I was, lying on his stomach in the summer grass, watching for hours while a tiny spider spun his web among the green blades. And the blades themselves, like all other plants, filled me with wonder, too. I sat open-mouthed before flowers and trees, silenced by my own awe at their clean, intricate, mysterious growth. Wide-eyed, I watched birds and chipmunks and butterflies and insects of every kind, as they went about the business of their lives. And I felt such a sense of privilege at seeing them, that sometimes I would shiver with sheer and quiet joy.

Then and through all the years that followed, I sought not so much to understand them as to celebrate them and that which bonds me to them: the simple fact of life itself.

Today, I am still more at home in a garden or a forest or upon the sea than I could ever be in the cities of man. For all their splendor, cities allow little or no room for the innocent, the small and the frail. And I have come to believe that life at its most vulnerable is life most clearly seen.

Perhaps that is the lesson I learned one night, long ago, when, as an infant, I wailed against the darkness and struggled to remain alive.

Some people dismiss the importance of sentiment, because it is based on fond remembrance. But I believe that the real business of life is the making of memories.

The quality of each day we live is largely determined by the attitude we bring to it. And our attitude is formed from that which is remembered of the experiences and the lessons of the past.

The time we have already lived is a personal legacy. In reflecting upon it, we may borrow from its wealth and enhance the richness of both the present and the future.

Often, I remember my grandparents. All four of them lived long and unique lives, but they passed away many years ago. In my mind's eye, however, I can still see their faces—drawn and lined, like maps of their lives. And in these old and smiling pictures I can feel the warmth of their presence and again know the gentleness of their wisdom. And, remembering them in their last years, I am reminded of how much the elderly have to give, and of the enduring pleasure their company can bring. And this memory becomes intent; for, each time I think of my own grandparents, I resolve to extend myself and my time to those who pre-date my own generation; to those whose memories are longer than mine; to those who, because of their age, are so often alone and neglected. And, often, in both my work and in my personal life, I act upon this resolve, and I know that my life is richer for it.

Memory bears such abundant fruit. The past times we have spent with our friends make us eager to be with them again. The reflected images of old loves remind us of the awkwardness of our young vulnerability and make us more grateful for what we have now. Or, if we have no special relationship, they remind us that we were and are worthy of love. The places we have been; the people we have known; the hours and years of remembered pleasure: these give us both the courage and the desire to rise from our beds in the morning and step out into the world and greet the new day as it comes. For this day, too, like those we have lived, will become a part of the wealth we bear and reflect its glow—through memory—on all of the time we have yet to live.

Love is not an occurence in our lives. Rather, it is a continuing process of growth.

We cannot say with certainty where or when its seed is first planted. In most instances it is probably transferred in the nurturing moments between parent and child. It seems to begin, therefore, with a specific intimacy between two separate lives; but it quickly becomes more generalized, embracing all living creatures. As the child grows, experiencing the difference between the kindly and the cold, love becomes more clearly defined. With increasing selectivity it moves outward, passing from shadow to sunlight; seeking the elements which will sustain it, allow it to flourish, extend its life.

When we experience adult love, therefore, it is the flower of an on-going pattern of life. Though its beauty may seem sudden, it has come through years of preparation. From seed to seedling; from sprout to plant to bud; its progression through the seasons has brought it to this shining moment.

But neither is love a single bloom. It does not stand in isolation. It moves to our friends and families, as if carried on the wind. And further still, it spreads to those who only just touch our lives, encouraging them by the witness of our example, to sow and nurture the seeds they bear; to open themselves and meet the sun.

In the end, then, love is a garden. In its ever-widening circle, it is the natural expression of our human potential. Whatever else we may do with the time of our lives, nothing can be of more enduring consequence than the hours we give to the health and growth of our own hearts.

On a deserted beach in Mexico; on the rocky coast of Maine; on the coral reefs that form the Florida Keys; wherever on earth the land meets the sea— there, I am most at home.

Through all of my childhood years, my family spent each summer at the New Jersey shore. We had a small, gray and white house one block from the ocean in the fishing village of Brielle. I grew up with sand in my shorts and in my shoes, and the gentle sound of the breaking waves became so familiar to me that their rhythm seemed to set the pace of my own life. Even now, years away from childhood and miles away from the nearest beach, if I close my eyes and concentrate, I can hear the sea: softly yet steadily calling to me, as if a bit of it had seeped into my own veins.

When the world of man becomes too close; when its chaos becomes so insistent that I feel my spirit sifting away, I know that it is time for me to return to the edge of the sea. There, perspective comes again. Beside that ageless immensity, all the trials of my own life are trivialized and eased away, like so many splints of driftwood, carried off by the ancient flow of a force man may know but never truly understand.

Among men, I am spiritually most at-ease while in the company of sailors and lighthouse-keepers; fishermen and divers. In their eyes one may always find an abiding humility: self-importance cannot thrive beside the power and wonder of the atmosphere in which they dwell. They know that the lifetime of any man is but a frail moment; that a few drops of water can douse the brightest flame.

Until my own light fails, I will continue to be drawn to the sea. Its gifts to me are a renewed sense of peace and an awareness of the measure of my place within the universe. With these, I may see the world with my eyes, my mind and my heart open—like a child on a beach, watching the waves unfurl before him for the very first time.

Perhaps I will never fully understand the longing that has so deeply characterized my life. I only know that it has been with me from the earliest times I can remember, and that it remains with me to this day: a quiet yet constant hunger to be joined with that which transcends this time and this place.

In my personal life I have sometimes found that this linkage is present within the sphere of human love. When I have been so fortunate as to touch and be touched by another, I have felt this yearning to be fulfilled. And yet, for me, the passage of time has inevitably changed or taken this love, and the longing has always returned.

It is in my work, both as an artist and a writer, that I have sensed the most certain and enduring movement toward both the object and the source of this yearning. I know with certainty that this is a spiritual quest, and in my work I have tried to explore those elements of human experience which allow us to see beyond the moment of our individual lives and to gaze upon that which is universal and immortal.

Though I subscribe to no conventional religion, I am partnered with those who humbly and reverently strive to see the face of God. The compulsion they feel is mine as well. Yet I cannot join them in their churches. Too often, I have seen the social character of these institutions lead them to become exclusive; and I have come to believe that the force that created life embraces all of life.

And so, I long. And so, I work. And, sometimes, when I am truly fortunate, I experience the joy that comes with the discovery of another link; a new connection; a continuance of the bond that spans all of time and joins every living creature. Then, at peace, my spirit may rest, renewing itself with the knowledge that I have moved one step nearer, one breath closer, to the power that awaits at the end of this quest. Then, morning comes, and—in its wondrous light—the longing and my journey begin again.

Time sweeps everything away. Like the ceaseless waves of a mighty sea, it dashes upon the shore of each human life, seizing the artifacts and elements with which we signify our existence; and—with neither disdain nor regard—it spirits them away. When it takes our sorrow or our despair, we may begin to believe that it is merciful. But when it steals beauty and innocence and charm and joy, we know that it is without compassion. Like the sea, time has no heart. It sweeps everything, and neither our resistance nor our regret can stay its flow.

Yet, knowing this, I am a beachcomber. As an artist and writer, I move upon time's shore, plucking pieces from the surf. Sometimes they are bits of my own life; sometimes treasures others have lost. In my work I put them into pictures or words—not that they might last forever, but that they may stay just a little longer; that others might know their tenderness or their light; and that, seeing these, they may more dearly value and fully experience the treasures within their own lives.

In a pack on my back, I carry pens, notebooks and a sketchpad wherever I go. These are the instruments of my hope. With them, I try to re-create the wonder I have found and to share it with whomever might pass my way.

My motivation rises more from gratitude than from charity. I have been extraordinarily fortunate in my life. I have been touched by many wonderful people; and I have seen places and events that have opened my senses and left me profoundly moved and deeply enriched. When fortune smiles upon us, I do not believe we can simply withold and contain its blessings. For me, it has become essential to share that which I have been privileged to know.

I would like to show you some of the pages from the sketchbook I carry. In the poems I have written upon them; in the stippled drawings which accompany them, I have tried to create pictures of feelings I have known. Now, they are yours to keep or to share with those you love. I give them to you, knowing that—for as long as you keep them; as long as they have meaning to you—they are safe from the ebb and flow of time. For so long as you hold them, they will not yet be lost. And that is the reason for a beachcomber's hope, as he leaves his home and rolls up his trousers and returns again to the edge of the sea.

UNTITLED #12

Love changes the essence of our lives. It brings a stillness to the center, and, with time, this inevitably flows into all that we do. In this way, that which we have received becomes a source of peace to all those who touch our world.

If the deepest part
of my life could speak,
then your heart would know
how I've been blessed
with grace and honor,
beyond all measure,
through these years
of loving you.

I believe in the power of prayer.

More than once in my life, I have found myself involved in situations that threatened to destroy not only my physical existence, but also the reasons for which I value this existence. Through prayer, I was given the courage to extricate myself from those patterns and the strength not merely to survive, but to grow.

Many people seem to think that they can exercise absolute control over their own lives. I have learned that this is an illusion, borne of shallow pride, and that the consequences for subscribing to such a conviction can be devastating.

When I am stressed by the more important decisions which must be made, I find a quiet place and separate myself from the world of man. There, I rest for a few moments. Then, I try to summarize the problem in a few words. And, having done that, I turn it over to the spiritual force that gave me life and ask for guidance. Then, I leave the problem alone.

Inevitably, the answer comes. It occurs so naturally that it seems as though it had been there all along.

I do not pray for money or material things. Those belong to the forces of earth. Rather, I ask for serenity, courage and wisdom. These are the gifts of the spirit. To ask for them is to trust that they will be given.

Some people go to churches and come away with their hearts filled with the blessings they find there.

I go to the beach or to the forest and come away with shells or pine cones or beautiful bits of wood. With these I dress my home, that I may always be mindful of God's gifts to man.

Wherever one may worship; however one may pray: these are incidental. That one does—in need or in thanksgiving—is all that really matters.

Toward the end of her career, Edith Piaf recorded a song that might have served as the anthem for her entire life. I would like to think of it as mine, as well. Loosely translated, its title is "No, I Will Have No Regrets."

With the exception of its partner, jealousy, no other human condition steals more time and energy than regret. When one is focused on what might have been, all the possibilities of the present slip away. They are consumed by a tired passion for a past that did not happen; and both the imagination and sense of adventure one might bring to this moment and to the future are smothered by the drabness of such reverie.

I believe that regret comes because most of us have a tendency to be far more critical of ourselves than we would ever be of others. We blame ourselves for not having the wisdom to have done things differently. With the benefit of hindsight to justify this, we are like scolding parents to ourselves. But few of our parents would be so unrelenting in their blame. In time, they would allow forgiveness to come; and if we are ever to move beyond regret, this is what we must allow ourselves.

We are not perfect. We do not enter the world that way, nor will we leave it that way. We make mistakes, and sometimes we learn from them. At other times we do precisely what should be done, but circumstances beyond our control alter the outcome we might have desired. Whatever the occasion may be, we remain imperfect people, living in an even more imperfect world; and if we fail to live up to our own expectations, perhaps they were too narrow to allow for that measure of imperfection.

Unchecked, regret becomes despair. If we can forgive ourselves for our fallibility and accept it as part of our humanity, we can begin to put an end to regret. Forgiveness clears the present and makes room for all the possibilities the future may hold. It opens the doors regret has closed; and, passing through them, we find the freshness and strength to dream new dreams, many of which may yet come true.

We forgive others for their limitations. If the songs of our lives are to be complete, we must be equally kind to ourselves.

It is in the company of our friends that we feel most fully alive. The love they give to us demands nothing more than the honest and spontaneous expression of all that we are. Yet, this exchange is so natural that we sometimes seem to take it for granted. And that, I believe, is unfortunate, for it dims our awareness of the extent to which these people grace our lives.

For each of us, the world is largely composed of strangers. As we move among them, we are aware of our own vulnerability; and, therefore, we keep our guards raised and withold our feelings, functioning only on the safest and most superficial level. We project a pleasant yet anonymous image, and this enables us to get through the day, untouched and unexposed.

I can only imagine how we would wither, if every day of our lives had to be lived in such a mannered and contained way.

Our friends open us. Their unwavering acceptance allows us to know and to experience the full range of our own potential. No joy and no sadness is too great to share with them. They allow us to laugh at ourselves and to laugh with them at the abundant foolishness within the world we share. In times of trouble, they console and counsel us and honor our humanity by the care with which they tend our frailty. They give us their secrets, and we give them our's; and, in this alliance of trust, we are freed of fear and unburdened of real or imagined guilt. In the atmosphere their presence creates, we live and we grow with the quiet knowledge that, through our follies and our triumphs, their tenderness remains constant and accessible and real.

It is difficult to express gratitude to people who continually give so much of themselves. In the closeness we have established with our friends, words of thanks seem awkward and out-of-place. And yet, the immensity of their generosity should not pass without recognition.

Only through our continuous and conscious resolve to be mindful of their importance to the quality of our lives can we do justice to our friends. Nothing more would be so dearly valued. But to give less than this would be to chance the self-indulgence that leads us to take them for granted.

The earliest feeling of love that I can remember was that which I felt for my father.

He was and is a quiet man, so that love had little to do with words. It grew from the instinctive trust I felt when I was in his presence.

When I was three years old, my mother decided that it was time for me to have my first barber-shop haircut. I don't know whether it was the word "cut" that terrorized me or the thought of going to a stranger who worked with scissors and razors; but, whatever it was, I wailed in horror.

With no deliberation my father lifted me into our old, black Plymouth and drove me down to the town of Bloomfield, where his barber plied his trade.

The shop itself was inside a dark, white-tiled tunnel, and, as our footsteps clicked on the marble floor, I was filled with a sense of doom.

But my Dad held my hand. He did not drag me along. Rather, in his straight-forward manner, he simply moved through that tunnel with total assurance. Then, in the bright, mirrored shop with the red-faced barber, smiling beside him, he held my hand all through the haircut. And, because he was so sure and unafraid, my fear gradually ebbed away; and my grip upon his fingers eased, and I felt much older, and the barber said I was "a fine, young man."

Afterwards, with the manly scents of hair tonic and witch hazel filling my nostrils, my Dad took me for ice cream. Then, all the way home, I sat tall and proud on the Plymouth's seat, so that everyone we passed would see that, now, I was no longer a baby; that I, indeed, had just had a barber-shop haircut; that, truly, I was "a fine, young man."

My Dad's hand taught me that love is trust. And, through all the love that I have known, that has been the most constant element and the one that I have most-dearly held.

A FATHER'S LOVE

You will find it in his eyes and in his hands, for these are the instruments of a man's soul. With tenderness and constancy it nurtures, guides, comforts and, above all, instills the trust that gives a child a reason to believe in this world.

A Father's love is a quiet thing,
    like the fall of footsteps on green grass
        and the sound of hope in the human heart.

When I think of my mother, I visualize a full circle of hope.

Her parents were Polish immigrants who came to this country with little money but a fortune in dreams. Like so many millions of their counterparts, their entire lives were spent in a day-by-day struggle to survive in the shadows of this, their promised land. At the end of their days, they had accumulated little more than a patch of earth and the simple artifacts for sustaining life. But this was their treasure, and it only re-affirmed their belief in the possibilities of the future.

My mother was their oldest daughter, and the expanded fulfillment of their dreams was passed to her. By the age of fourteen her formal education was ended, and she was working full-time at the first in a series of grueling, unskilled jobs. Nearly every penny she would earn for the next ten years went to her parents for the support of her brothers and sisters.

After she met and married my father, she continued to work, for the pre-eminent lesson of her young life had been that work equals hope. Later, when my sister and brother and I were born, she set aside that ethic for a while, replacing it with the only other value to which she has given credence: the nurturing of a family. But when Mary Ellen, Peter and I had trundled off to school, she went back to work as a sales clerk, a crossing-guard, a house-keeper; beginning again the litany of hours and days and years of meager wages, which when gathered together might allow for the realization of another step forward, a hope sustained.

Today she dreams of winning the New Jersey lottery or the Irish Sweep-stakes. Now, it is only by the whim of chance that her lifetime of hope will find its fullest fruition. But she believes in this with the same intensity that she gave to the conviction that every hour of work would bring her nearer to the better life, as she and her parents imagined it might be.

I know now that the hope that has governed my own life was instilled by my mother's hand. It is a legacy I have come to cherish, for though disappoint-ment and frustration have often crossed my path, hope has always allowed me to see beyond them; to summon the strength to travel the extra mile; to imag-ine a world that does not yet exist, but may exist in some future time, if one just believes hard enough and wills and works to see it through.

Twelve miles north of San Francisco, there is a place of deep and enduring serenity. When the world of man becomes close and insistent; when its touch is furtive, and its voice grows harsh, my spirit remembers and carries my body across those miles to the quiet splendor that is Muir Woods.

For me and for thousands of others, this is a healing place. Spread beneath the gentle slope of Mt. Tamalpais, this ancient grove of redwoods stands like an extended family of silent sages, whose presence alone communicates both a sense of wonder at the fact of life itself and the brevity of the moment of every man. In the shade and shelter of these towering trees, one is inevitably reminded that they were here long before we came and that they will remain long after all traces of our lives have vanished. Yet—strangely; magically—the humility that this awareness inspires does not diminish the dignity of man. Rather, it renews and enhances it by turning our focus toward that which is truly important within our lives and away from the trivial and parasitic elements which drain our energy and burden our minds.

The preservation of the Woods is intended to commemorate the life and works of the naturalist, John Muir. His efforts were a celebration of life on earth; and today this bit of land remains a verdant example of the balance that is necessary for life to continue and to thrive.

In an age when stress seems to have become an integral part of human existence, I believe that it is urgent for each of us to find such a place and to return to it often, that we may retain a sense of perspective with regard to our lives in an increasingly public world. While I am fortunate to have these woods near-at-hand, others may turn to the sea for their solace. Still more people may find their peace in any of the vast number of parks and forests that grace this land. And in the gardens they tend in their own backyards, still others may experience the rhythm and the flow of life and, through its observation, retain a sense of their place within the universe.

For, to see life clearly, it is often necessary to step away from the narrow patterns of one's everyday existence. Without the guidance of this greater vision, one maintains only the perspective of a spider who spins and toils through all the day, yet never sees the world as anything but a web.

She had a voice like a soft fog-horn and a smile that seemed to contain a piece of the sun. Through the years, when she has flared back into my mind, she has always worn the same yellow dress: the one she wore that night I kissed her beneath the paper lanterns, as we danced at the Junior Prom.

Her name was Bonnie; and I had just turned 17; and all through that shining spring, I thought of nothing and no one else. Only that which attended her had meaning to me. But everything that attended her—the words she spoke; the dreams we shared; her laughter every time we met; her wistful gaze when she did not know that I had seen—each of these were of monumental concern to me.

I could not imagine how anyone could not love her; and yet I was certain that no one could love her more than I.

And she said she loved me, too; and she cried when my parents said that I would have to go away with them for the summer; and September seemed like years away; yet she wrote every day through June and July; and I did, too: funny letters, etched with yearning; until August came, and my feet were burning, as I walked back from the mailbox, along the drive in front of our place in Brielle, empty-handed; eighty miles away from her; writing still, but desperately, for her letters came less frequently and, finally, not at all, through the last two weeks of that searing month; and I invented reasons for her silence; consoling excuses; lies to myself, until the first of September came.

Then, home in Caldwell, I ran all the way to her house, And, when she opened the door, I could see through the summer screen that her smile was a prelude; a hesitation; a shadow; a gesture; a consideration, extended to me; awkwardly; until she found the courage to say *his* name.

Numbly, I walked back to my parents' house and wrote her a letter. I told her then I would never forget her. And all through the years of other affections, I kept that promise to her.

First love is a season in the time of the heart. It aches, and it breaks; and it tears us apart. We abandon our own to the light of another; we live in their brightness and imagine no other; till that light becomes but a flickering ember, that burns through all time and makes us remember, that love, above all, is something we give; and life without love is no life to live.

Those who find love early and easily may not fully understand its power. Those who have lost love and known its sorrow have learned that its splendor is worthy of awe.

To love is truly an act of courage. It is a confrontation not only with our own vulnerability in the world of man, but also with the consequence of our own mortality. To contend with these forces is to chance great pain. Those who dare to love take that risk, and their valor adds both dignity and honor to the human condition.

In the world of man, each of us is subject to the chaos of time and change. To commit oneself to another; to vow fidelity; to share one's frailty and dreams: these are acts of individual merit, for they stand against the uncertainty and disenchantment which are the legacy of such a world.

But to go beyond even that; to state one's resolve to be joined through eternity; to stand with one's beloved, while knowing that parting is death's bequest: these are the bold and shining assertions of one who believes that life is a gift and that it has no value unless it is lived.

By their courage those who love affirm their belief in human life. They have not withdrawn; they have not grown bitter. They have not allowed fear to diminish them. Rather, they have seen the shadow of its face and chosen to light a candle against despair.

And, through all the generations, their candle is the beacon by which each of us have been born.

When love enters our lives, everything changes. The most ordinary of our surroundings acquire a freshness; a crisp and vivid clarity. Old, familiar songs suddenly seem laden with truth and wisdom. Colors become more intense. Time expands, as we mark its passage, no longer in weeks or months, but in the hours and minutes apart from the one we love. Strangers seem friendlier; friends, more dear, as smiles come easily, and the little things that might have troubled us in the past become so small that they fade from sight. And the future—that vague, uncertain passage just ahead—beckons and fills with promise; for every hope and dream we had now becomes distinctly possible and even more wondrous, in light of the prospect that we may share the delight they will bring with someone who knows and understands and embraces our gladness.

I believe that it is in this future-sight that the most enduring facet of love is shown. At its core is companionship: not the occasional joining one might anticipate with acquaintances or friends, but the constant, spiritual communion that weaves the two individuals into a single thread, which transcends time. It is their desire, their enthusiasm and their unselfish determination that binds them and, thus, allows them to see that which is to come as inevitably rich and full and real.

Love changes everything. But, most particularly, it gives light and strength to our vision of all that is yet to be. Partnered, our resources are more than doubled, for hope becomes reality in the rare and nurturing company we keep.

As the world in deepest winter sleeps beneath a shell of frost and snow, so does the wisdom of the heart, until love—like the sun—dissolves its shield and beckons it to grow.

With the coming of love, each succeeding day of our lives acquires a wholeness and depth. We do not merely share the person we were nor simply adjust our dreams to include another. Rather, we begin again. In this new time we perceive ourselves within a pair, and the dreams we now conceive are born of that perception.

As the seasons progress, and our trust in one another deepens, our growing closeness allows us to experience the world through each other's senses. Our vision is broadened; our understanding, enhanced; our judgements, rendered with greater compassion. Those who have never known love might think that our individuality is thereby compromised; and this would doubtlessly be true if love were not exchanged. But in our sharing, that which we give is compounded by what we receive; and our individuality is extended and given greater insight.

With the continued passage of time, we may also seem to take life more seriously. Our values become less transient, as our commitment to one another creates a clear sense of responsibility. Instinctively we are moved to protect that which binds us and to exercise care in all that pertains to the health of our union. In the light of this same regard, our hopes and intentions are formed. These now acquire substance, for they no longer rise from our own whim or fantasy. Instead, they are shaped by our common vision of the life we wish to share.

All of these changes occur so naturally that we seldom realize how profound they are. Only when memory carries us back to the long years of our own winter do we truly see how far we have come and begin to know how fortunate we are. Perhaps it is with this gentle reminder that the heart shows its final wisdom and turns us back toward the sun and to all the years we have yet to share.

UNTITLED #14

*If words could say all that we feel, there would be no need
for an embrace. But language has its limitations,
and the heart has none. It expresses itself spontaneously
in even the smallest things we do.*

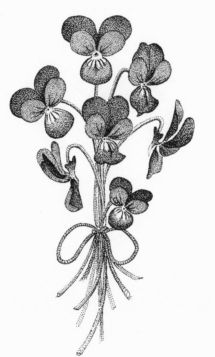

Sometimes
    your nearness
        takes my breath away;
    and all the things
    I want to say
        can find no voice.
    Then, in silence,
    I can only hope
        my eyes
            will speak
                my heart.

It is the presence of nurturing that validates love. Without this characteristic, our involvement with another is a purely self-centered activity. With it, we focus our concerns beyond our own gratification and tend to the welfare of the one who has touched our lives.

This is an entirely natural tendency, but the knowledge required to effectively care for another can only come with time. For it is the knowledge of our loved one's strengths and needs that allows us to give ourselves to that which will encourage their health and growth. Also, it is the knowledge of their weaknesses that gives us the vision to tend to these with compassion, without encouraging the harm of their expansion.

While nurturing always includes an element of kindness, it is more than kindess alone. It is a commitment to that vision of a shared future; a continuous flow of specific encouragement; a consistent tenderness; and a resolute resistance to all that might come between us. It requires time, and it is the one aspect of love that demands our objectivity. But, with the rest of our lives before us, nothing could be of greater importance.

I believe there is a direct correlation between the health of a relationship between two people and the degree to which the element of hope exists within that relationship.

When we intend to build a life together, both the quality and the direction of our common aspirations act as our guide into the years that lay before us. If these are based upon our knowledge of ourselves as individuals; if we truly believe we have the ability and the tenacity to achieve the realization of these dreams; if we have communicated them to one another and allowed them to become a vision of the future to which we may both be committed: then we have given our pairing a reason and a destiny.

If, however, our partnership is merely based upon whimsey or the pleasure of the moment; if our expectations are traced from images of great wealth or glamour or power; if we have not taken the time to know the extent and potential of our own abilities: then our hope is without promise, and we may soon find our union threatened by the inevitable awareness that is has nowhere to go.

If we love one another, we truly want the best for one another. We are capable of giving that when we have taken the time and allowed the honesty that will align and refine the dreams we share. Hope is the force that will carry us through all the days that are yet to come. If our passage is to be as certain as life will allow, we must both clearly see the path we will follow.

The integrity and depth of any form of human love can truly be measured by the degree to which the element of trust exists within that union.

Whether we wish to initiate, to sustain or to encourage the growth of a relationship, no other single factor should be given more abiding concern. For without trust, no vow has substance; no promise has merit; no words of endearment can be regarded as anything more than good intentions.

A sense of intimacy is the central manifestation of love. This can only exist when two people feel free to express any confidence; to reveal their awkwardness and frailty; to give all that they are, knowing that each dimension of their lives will be embraced and safeguarded.

This profound exchange is a natural flow when trust is present. But if that element is shaken or removed, intimacy is displaced by self-consciousness, hesitation and reserve. In their presence love is diminished; and, if trust cannot be restored, the relationship may only exist as a shadow of what it was.

Between spouses, lovers, relatives and friends, the bond that is spun is composed of a myriad of different fibers. But whenever it is evident that two people deeply cherish one another, one can be certain that trust is at the core of their bond.

Whatever else one may learn of love, I believe that its essential import must remain secondary to this.

Love is a seed. Sometimes it is planted in fertile ground, and it grows and blossoms and gives splendor to our lives. At other times, however, it is planted in sand, and that element contains nothing that will nourish the seed. Left there, it languishes and dries and eventually dies.

At some point in our lives, each of us will be hurt by giving our love to someone who cannot or will not give theirs in return. If we are sensitive people, we will find this difficult to accept and to understand, for we know the value of this gift. But, if we are to avoid extraordinary and lingering pain, we must recognize this when it does occur, and we must bring ourselves to action.

Books have been written about how to heal a wounded heart. They advise an emphasis on the company of friends; a change of atmosphere; a packing away of all those artifacts which remind us of the person who filled our immediate past.

But more important than these, I believe, is the need to be continually mindful of the fact that we are worthy of love and that, just beyond our vision, there is someone out there who yearns to hold what we have to give. And, above all, it is essential to recognize that we have the ability to give love. This is a rare quality, and it must never be taken for granted.

The degree to which we concentrate on the present and the future will determine how quickly the past will become the past. In the company of a friend; with no physical reminders to stir the dust; in places which afford us the opportunity to reawaken our sense of discovery: we will begin to truly live again.

In the end sand is of little consequence. It cannot nourish a seed, but it does slip easily through an hour-glass, and it is quickly carried off by time and the wind.

UNTITLED #15

*The quality of the life we have known together gives us
substance and continuity. That which is dearly remembered
graces not only the present but also our vision
of all we have yet to share.*

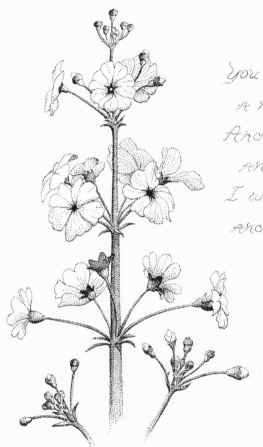

You have given me
a mountain of memories.
And when we are old
and tired and worn,
I will take your hand,
and we will climb to its peak
and have all this joy
to know again.

When one finds so much beauty in the world, the ideal would be to share it with one particular person. But the finding of love is a fortunate accident: when the elements of time and circumstance converge, some people are blessed, while others must continue to make their way alone.

Perhaps it is because I have spent so many years on my own that I have sought to share this beauty with others through my work. Without this opening, I am certain that my heart would be weighted by having to contain the joy and enthusiasm I have found.

That you are here, and that through these words you may travel with me and share some of the wonder I have been privileged to know: this makes my journey through life far more satisfying than it might have been. And, for that good fortune, I always try to remember that, on the other side of these sentences, there is a person who is worthy of the affection and respect that I would give to a friend.

It was a simple, white, two-story house on a quiet street in the town of Caldwell, New Jersey. All around it there were trees which my father had planted: apples and pears; cherries and chestnuts; peaches, and one tall and spreading maple, which had been there for years before we came. Beneath these trees, there was further evidence of my father's skill and care: a sweet half-circle of honeysuckle bordered one side of the quarter-acre lot; raspberry bushes dressed the backyard, beside a small garden of tomatoes and lettuce and peas. And on each side of the house, there was grass: not the patchy stubble so often seen today, but a rich, unbroken blanket of green.

In the house itself there were seven rooms: a bright yellow kitchen, where my mother always seemed to be; a seldom-used living room; a separate dining room which opened to a huge back porch: a sun-parlor, where our Christmas tree was always placed; and three bedrooms—my folks', my sister's, and the large one, overlooking the back porch, which my brothers and I shared.

We lived in this house for fifteen years; and it is the place that comes to my mind whenever I hear someone speak longingly of "home." In my mind's eye its rooms are crowded with memories. But what I remember most are the little things about the place that made it ours: the pencil marks my parents made on the door frames, recording our growth; my father's neat but much-used workbench in the cool cellar; my mother's African violets—pink and purple—spread across the dining room window sill; a crayon sketch of a little girl on my sister's wall, that a nun had done and given to my folks the day Mary Ellen was born; my brother's wagon, over-flowing with hand-me-down toys; and the window beside my bed, through which I passed in secret, midnight journeys, to lie on my back, atop the porch roof, and stare at the stars and wonder where my life would take me. From where I lay, I could see the lights on the far, western hills. But I never imagined how far beyond them I would eventually go.

When I entered college, my folks moved to a beautiful house in the south-central part of the State. My mother called it their "dream-house," but I spent so little time there that it was never home to me. Later, they, too, left it behind for the dubious charms of South Florida. And, finally, when my youngest brother had grown and gone off to college, they returned to New Jersey; this time settling into a neat brick house in a nervous retirement community at the Shore.

Three years ago during the Christmas season, I visited them at this last address. Restless in their new surroundings, I asked my folks if they would like to drive to Caldwell, to see the old place again. My mother and my sister said they would.

In my rented Toyota we drove the eighty miles northward and easily found Caldwell. It was little changed. We passed the church we had attended; the malt shop; the toy store, where I had worked; the markets; the garden apartments; the schools. Each of these seemed much the same, yet slightly smaller: memory had painted them in broader strokes. The familiar streets were still familiar; and as we drove down Academy Road, we knew we were almost there.

Turning the corner into Prospect Street, I immediately realized that this had been a mistake. This was a trip we should never have taken.

The house was still there, but it had been painted a dismal olive green. The trees were gone: all of them. The honeysuckle, too, had been torn away and replaced by grass, the color of thatch. Wind-blown newspapers littered the lawn. All of the windows were dark; all of the shades were drawn. Someone lived there; but no one was home.

We sat silent in the car, each of us searching for some detail that might not have been changed. But there was so little left of what we had known that, when the winter sun set behind the house a few minutes later, each of us felt drained, diminished; cold and bare.

"Now we know," my mother said softly.

We turned away, knowing we would not go there again. We did not look back; none of us chose to compound our regret.

"Thank goodness, we didn't see the inside," my sister said.

Thank goodness, indeed. Now and for all time, those pencil marks may still remain beside the doors; the workbench and the African violets and the toys and that picture of the little girl may be undisturbed. And I can still look through that window again, knowing my brothers are sleeping safely behind me, and choose—not the roof nor my wandering dreams—but to remain with them in the sweet and quiet place, through each day of my life; for as long as I live.

For in the chill half-light of that winter day, I came to realize that home is a place we carry within us; its occupants are the people we love. Neither knowledge nor the hand of man can change it: that which was ever will be in that remembered place, deep in our hearts, where our dreams began, and where they will always belong.

In the backpocket of my mind, I carry a picture of my sister, Mary Ellen. In this creased and slightly-yellowed photograph, she is forever eleven years old. She is wearing a plaid, cotton dress; and her skinny limbs reveal none of the grace she was later to acquire. With prominent elbows, her arms hang loosely at her sides, while her fingers pinch the skirt of that summer dress. Slightly knock-kneed, she stands in a pair of Buster Browns: those chunky, inelegant shoes our mother always referred to as "sensible." Her just-washed hair is dark and straight; and a breeze in that long-ago July or August day has lifted her bangs, revealing her shyly crinkled eyes. She is smiling (she always seemed to be smiling then;) and the singular quality her face presents is a delicate sweetness; a bashful innocence; an endearing femininity, so quietly evident that any brother or any man would be tendered by its fragile force.

Now, though the years have given my sister surety and sophistication, professional competence and pragmatic wisdom, when I see her in an off-guard moment, she retains the essence of that little girl. Though she has grown into the world, she has never completely grown away from the child she was in that summer of her eleventh year. And as I—her equally awkward, but never-so-innocent younger brother—was befuddled then by the gentle power she held over me, I remain irredeemably mystified by the silent authority she continues to bear. It is as if she carried some age-old secret within her: one that I could never know nor hope to understand. And perhaps because she knows this, too, and has seen the advantage it naturally affords, she has never used it willfully; rather, she has left it to spin its perpetual wonder on its own.

As adults, Mary Ellen and I have become great friends. Often, we travel together, sharing the same pleasures; seeing the same sights. But—every so often—from the corner of my eye, I catch a glimpse of that mystery again; and I know she is seeing something I can't see; or hearing some song I never will know; or feeling some feeling beyond all my feelings: adrift in a daydream; lost in a glow.

A brother can always cope with a brother: nature has made them like peas in a pod. But a sister is ever a smiling enigma: a child in a photo, taken by God.

THE CHILDREN OF SUMMER

*With brothers and sisters; with companions and friends;
the passage of time is measured only by the increasing richness
of the memories we share. By the joining of our hearts,
we transcend age and retain both our sense of play and our freedom
to become all that we are.*

We will always be children
    in the time of the heart;
  for trust never ages, and love has no end.

Because my brother, Peter, is two years younger than I, in my mind he has always remained essentially a little boy. Through the years when we were growing up, we shared the same room; yet, while my disposition grew more and more intense, his remained light-hearted and sunny. He laughed easily; and with his open smile he made a quick friend of any person he met.

More like our Dad, I was quiet and bookish, and I tended toward skepticism when encountering new people or experiences. While I envied Peter's ease, I thought of him as vulnerable because of it; and I developed a protectiveness toward him, extending my role of big brother well into our adult lives.

Though he has been married for several years and has three young children of his own, in my heart he is still six years old; and when I see him there, he is laughing through some summer day, running through an open field with a puppy at his heels.

Two years ago he suffered a cardiac arrest. Running in a marathon, he collapsed. He was rushed to a hospital and, shortly thereafter, underwent a triple bypass. While my parents, my sister and my brother rushed to his side, three-thousand miles separated Pete and I. At my folks' insistence I remained on the West Coast, hovering over the phone; frantic; helpless; feeling evermore a failure in my role as protector. That my younger brother should be threatened by death; that he might die while I lived: this I had never imagined. That he needed me, and there was nothing I could do: this seemed like the cruelest violation of an unspoken trust.

Late into that night of his deepest vulnerability, I sat on the steps in front of my home, murmuring at the heavens; fearing the worst; feeling utterly useless. In the darkness I paced the sidewalk, never far from the phone on the porch; and as the leaden hours passed, I knew with more and more certainty that he was slipping away.

Finally, there came a moment of clear and certain despair. I sat on the steps and knew that Pete—at that same instant—lay balanced on the breath-wide line between life and death. I buried my head in my arms and summoned every last ounce of faith. Aloud, between gritted teeth, I told God to take my strength and give it to my brother, that he might live. It was less a prayer than an order, for I felt no humility—only purest love.

There was no pause. There was a sudden rushing sound; and though my eyes were closed, I saw an arc of silver light leave my body, race into the star-lit eastern sky and, in a final flash, disappear. Then, for an instant, there was total darkness.

When I opened my eyes and raised my head, I knew Pete would be all right. It was not a wish: it was a certainty. I felt exhausted but completely at peace. I thanked God; went inside; lay down on my bed and instantly fell to sleep.

My mother's call the next morning awakened me. She told me that Pete had suddenly rallied; was much better; would be all right. She only confirmed what I already knew.

The following Christmas, I went to North Carolina and spent the holidays with Pete and his family. In one of those midnight talks to which brothers are prone, I told him of what I had felt and what I had experienced on that August night, when he lay so near to death.

He said he already knew. Though he had been unconscious, he remembered with instinctive clarity that an arc of silver light had come to him and that he had reached for it, knowing that it was my strength, and that I had sent it to him. Though I had said very little, he described that instant with the same accuracy and off-hand ease with which he might have told me, years before, of a field-mouse he had met one afternoon, while playing in the grass behind our house.

Between brothers, there is a quiet understanding that—no matter what forces may be altered by time and distance—nothing between them ever will change. Wherever one may go, the other, too, is there. Like concentric circles, they are forever joined by the love that is their core.

Before my youngest brother, Tom, was born, we were a family in the throes of quiet disintegration. My sister and I had crossed into our teens; my brother, Pete, was at their threshold. Each of us had begun to define our lives by our widely disparate interests. Mary Ellen was a twirler, and the little free time she had was spent in the chatty company of her girlfriends. I was running in a dozen different directions at once, trying to be popular among my classmates by commiting all of my energy to each of a hundred high-school activities. Pete was everywhere but at home; and, to this day, if asked about his whereabouts during those years, he will smile and say he was "out" and nothing more. We saw each other only occasionally in the evening and then by the gray light of the television set.

My parents, too, seemed to be at an unspoken breach: my father, evermore consumed by his job; my mother, singing her heart out at choir-practice, or nursing any one of the many old ladies who lived in our neighborhood back to full and semi-vigorous health.

Then Tom came along.

The first time I saw him, I nicknamed him "B.B."—short for "bowling ball," to which his head bore a striking resemblance. Immediately, I named myself his protector: nothing was going to happen to this fat and cheerful little kid while I was around. My sister became an instant expert on child-rearing. Though she had outgrown any interest in dolls, here was one to re-kindle that fancy. On the night of his birth, she baked a batch of blue cupcakes to celebrate his arrival. These were never eaten: Pete used them appropriately for softball practice. For his part, Peter saw Tom as a cross between a toy and a friend: a squirming, gurgling and, eventually, walking teddybear; and he dragged him along as a silent witness to many of his mysterious adventures.

We thought it was odd when my dad started coming home early from work, but it was even more peculiar when my mother quit the choir and told the old ladies they would have to fend for themselves for a while. Suddenly, we were a unit again—five, instant, would-be parents and one innocent and receptive charge.

That Tom was big enough to contain all of the love and guidance we poured into him attests to his resilience. He neither questioned nor sorted it; and he never favored one of us above the others. He took what each of us had to give and returned the full and cheerful measure of his own affection. Drawn to him, we were drawn to one another again. We became, not the family we had been, but a new, stronger and far more tender one.

Tom is a teacher today. If his effect upon our family can be transferred to his colleagues and students, several generations of young people may be enriched by his wisdom and love. Even in his innocence he gave it to us. Now, with maturity and a sense of purpose he extends it, too, to the family of man.

Of all the towns and cities I have seen, only a few have remained within me long after the business of life has carried me away from them.

As there are people in the world who are "right" for us, there are places where we feel most certainly alive. Something about their particular atmospheres touches a point in our hearts or our minds, and we find—quite suddenly—that we are living more intensely and experiencing more intimately than might have been possible anywhere else.

Over the years I have discovered this magical quality in Lugano, Switzerland, particularly after the brief, summer showers have lifted the heat from its cobblestone streets; in Key West, Florida, when the early autumn sunsets signal the start of sweetly sensuous nights; in New Orleans, where even the air tastes like the finest meal one might ever eat; in Paris, where the ghosts of all the world's great lovers seem to gather, when twilight streaks the western sky.

Several years ago, while vacationing in California, I found it again in the fog-muted colors and sea-scented air of San Francisco. The dizzying topography of the city; the Victorian lunacy of its architecture; the free and smiling attitude of its people: these all combined and spun an irresistible cord, that would not let me slip away. I had planned to stay two weeks; I stayed seven. Returning to the state where I had been living, I settled my affairs; said a few hasty good-byes; loaded my car; and moved to the Bay Area, where I have been living, contendedly and productively, ever since. Even at this extended and close proximity, the city has retained its magic for me, and I cannot imagine making my home anywhere far from this softly shimmering place.

My wanderlust remains, however. Whenever I am able, I journey toward some place I have never seen. Recently, I found another magic city—Quebec; and if I close my eyes, the snowy winter days I passed in its coffee houses and splendid little shops seem just a breath or two away. For reasons I do not know, I was able to write some wonderful passages there, and this alone makes me eager to return.

I have come to believe that travel is essential to our growth as human beings. As no single person can fill all of our needs, no single place can stimulate all of the elements of our potential. But—out there—just beyond the horizon, among those places we have never seen, there are parts of our lives; waiting; beckoning for us to come and live them through.

POSTCARD / Sunday Morning

*Those who have given us the freedom to love have opened our hearts
and filled those once-quiet chambers with the warmth of their presence.
Whether we are together or apart, they remain within us,
and the wonder they made possible continues to flow.*

Sunday morning

POSTCARD

USA
22
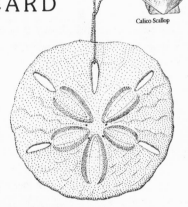
Calico Scallop

you will never be more
than a breath away
from the center
of my heart.

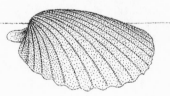

The one human virtue that I have come to admire above all others is simple kindness. Today I find it most often among elderly people, and they tell me that they remember a time when it was common. But the competitive society to which we have evolved seems to have spun a coarseness, a combative element of self-interest, into our national character; and kindness has been displaced by more aggressive "values."

Still, by its rarity the merit of kindness has only been enhanced. Occasionally we hear people say that a particular person has "truly made a difference" in their lives. Inevitably, the difference came because that person stepped out of the flow of self-absorbed men and women and gave a bit of time and care to another human being. This is more than a superficial gesture of charity. It is a conscious choice to extend one's talents and concern to another person's welfare.

Often we hear people say that one has to be hard and tough to survive in the world today. The implication of such an attitude is that any degree of self-sacrifice is a sign of weakness. I wonder what quality can possibly come to a life governed by such cynicism. In the process of living from day to day, how can there by any joy or satisfaction? The malignant presence of fear and loathing seem a much more likely prospect.

Kindness requires so little. It is composed of gentleness, tolerance and a respect for the dignity of others. It costs nothing. But when a person chooses to exercise it, they reveal their own belief in the value of life itself. And when they rest their heads at night, the rewards of having lived another day must be evident in the peace that comes to them.

Wisdom need not only come with age. If one chooses to be kind, it can also be an act of the will.

We seldom know the influence of the words we speak, for we cannot see into the hearts of those who hear them. But language has power to wither or heal; and, if we are to avoid victimizing others, the manner in which we address them must be guided by a respect for their humanity.

Of all the people who have had an enduring effect upon my life, the one who comes most readily to mind in this regard is John Almquist. He was one of my professors during my junior year of college, and his course was both challenging and stimulating. He peppered my mind with ideas, and I worked intensely to refine them, expand them, apply them. And just as some of these would become clear, he would send an avalanche of new ideas barreling down, and I would reach for them, hoping to contain them all.

At the end of the course, a major project was due. I worked feverishly to create something that would indicate how intellectually alive his course had made me feel. Night after long night, I filled pages with what I imagined were original thoughts, trying to assemble them into a single, coherent whole. But— at the end—all my efforts came to nothing. I could not hand in the paper I had written; it seemed thoroughly inept and incomplete.

On the last day of the course, I went to Mr. Almquist to apologize for not being able to turn in the project. I was bitterly disappointed with myself.

He brushed aside my apology. He said, "Sexton, I've seen you work. I've seen your reach, and I know that will not stop. I believe in you. If you remember nothing else I've taught you, remember that."

He gave me the highest possible grade for the course. But more than that, he gave me the assurance that I was of value. He believed in me; and he believed in my writing; and he was the first person who ever took the time to let me know that.

Over the years his words have come back to me again and again. Through all the rejection slips; through all the admonitions to "do this as a hobby;" his words kept me going when others advised a simpler, safer life.

The words he chose have become a beacon to me. If each of us would only try to be aware of the influence of what we say, I believe all of us might find our paths more brightly-lit.

Loneliness is not a wayward thing. It is neither a chill wind nor a vagrant fog. It does not simply roll out of the blue and fall upon an innocent victim, tingeing their day or night with its dank and shapeless desolation.

Loneliness is quite specific. It comes to those who have not given enough love and to those who have given, narrowly and without wisdom, to people and things which cannot love them in return.

I believe that we have been made with pockets in our lives, and that these have been left open, so that others may fill them with the love they bring to us. When these spaces are neglected and remain empty for long periods of time, they expand and become yawning vacuums, pleading to be filled. And, when there is not love enough within or around us, loneliness answers and settles within these voids, and its dark spectre becomes impossible for us to ignore.

When loneliness comes to me, I have no power to contend with it, until I accept the fact that I have called it upon myself. I cannot blame others for its presence; if I had extended my love to them, they would be with me now. It is in this acceptance that I may begin to open my life; to rearrange its priorities; to initiate a flow of human concern with those who are capable of accepting my affection and able and eager to share their own.

If we assume responsibility for its presence, loneliness can serve as a not-so-gentle reminder that our need for one another is also the source of our most enduring joy.

Not long ago I walked through the National Cemetery at the Presidio in San Francisco. It was late afternoon, and the mauve and rosey colors of the gathering dusk tinted the headstones on the graves of the thousands of young people who rest within that solemn and beautiful place.

All around me there were sensations of life: birds, chattering sweetly in the nearby trees; a passenger plane, scratching the sky, high overhead; the vivid colors of autumn; and the soft, life-bearing wind that rustled my collar and rolled across the gently sloping land.

Yet, at my feet, there was only the silence of lives that had ended much too soon.

I paused before one shadowed grave, and, looking down into the rich, green grass that was its blanket, I thanked the young man who lay within. His sacrifice had assured my freedom; and, though I sometimes seem to take that for granted, on this day, in this place, I could not. For just behind this young man, there slept another. And behind him, another. And row after row of individual lives spread before me, each unique and born with hope; each now closed and sealed in silence by the tongues and hands of tyranny.

It is the courage and generosity of those who died for freedom that has given me my own. Their legacy is my gift, and I hold it with both gratitude and a sense of responsibility.

Standing among them in that hallowed place, I felt their purpose and their resolve. For tyranny still walks upon this earth, and, whether it wears the armor of dictatorial authority or clothes itself in the mantle of self-righteous, religious zeal, its quest is the same: the denial of individual liberty.

If I am to honor their bequest and to pass its richness to those who follow me, then my life must be both a celebration of individual freedom and a vigilant defense against its enemies. Human history has shown that one cannot live without the other: defense without conscience becomes offence; liberty without caution is a timid prey.

Through the fading light of that afternoon, I lingered as with a company of friends, and felt the measure of the faith they had held for every man and me.

HERITAGE

*Our presence here is a gift. In turn, we must resolve
to conserve this garden by moving along its paths with
intelligence, respect and humility. If we do, our lives
will enrich this place. If we do not, we abuse not only the gift,
but the Giver, as well.*

Be gentle
    with the earth,
for heaven has entrusted
    its care to us
and bound the future
of each living thing
to the heart and hand
        of man.

Shortly after the turn of the century, my grandfather emigrated to this country from Poland.

I don't know what his dreams were when he came to the United States, but I suspect that many of them came true. As a young man he built the house on Liberty Street in Bloomfield, New Jersey, that would be his home for the rest of his life. There he lived and raised a family with his first wife, until she died giving birth to their seventh child. Then he married my grandmother, and they added four more children to that home.

Because he died when I was very young, I have few specific memories of him. Still, in all but one of these, he seemed to be a happy man. He loved his family and took great pride in his grandchildren. He loved the vineyard he tended in his yard and relished the wine he made from its purple grapes. Often, as I sat on his lap beneath a bee-spun arbor, he would kiss my cheek, and his whole body would shake with laughter, when I cringed at the roughness of his beard.

But I remember a Sunday when he did not laugh, and his smile did not reach to his eyes. Beneath the arbor on that fine summer day, I asked him why he was sad. He shook his heavy head and would not tell me at first. But I persisted; and finally, quietly, he told me this:

In his sleep the night before he had seen the world come to an end. It had been destroyed by fire. His house was gone; his yard and vines were gone. That town, that state, this country, this earth: all of these were gone. And all the people he loved, and all the people he had never had a chance to know: these were gone as well. Everything was burned to ashes. And the terrible part was that God had not done this thing. It had been done by man, because he had not been wise or careful. And from this now-awful place, God had gone, too. Man had broken His heart, and he had gone away, because He could not bear the shame.

My grandfather was silent then. He looked around the bright richness of his yard, but that day it did not bring joy to his face.

"It was only a dream, Grandpa," I told him.

He looked down into my eyes and smiled; but the sadness remained, like a shadow on his brow.

"Yes," he said softly. "It was only a dream."

He was in his early eighties then, and he would only live a few years longer. But through all the times I saw him after that day, he again seemed to be a happy man. He had given his best to life; and life in turn had been good to him. So many of his dreams had come true.

The dream he shared with me that warm afternoon in his vineyard has remained in my mind, like the music of a strange song, heard only once, but never-after quite forgotten. As I grew into manhood, I dismissed it for a while as a figment of his intrinsic Polish melancholy. But that did not extinguish it.

Every so often it would come back into my mind, particularly in those moments when I saw or experienced something of fragile beauty. Now that I have travelled far from my early home and seen many parts of the world, I have learned that all beauty is fragile, and yet—for the moment—it flourishes everywhere. But knowing that, the memory of his dream has flourished for me, as well.

My grandfather died in his sleep in 1952. He was 87 years old.

He knew nothing of nuclear proliferation.

He could not have imagined a world with 50,000 warheads.

He knew only his family and his garden. Life had taught him that both of these required care. But life had also taught him that, among the inhabitants of this earth, there were careless men.

I will never forget the abundant kindness of his nature nor the fullness of his life. But neither can I forget the deep sadness in his face when he spoke of that dream.

My grandfather is gone.

But the careless men who scorched his sleep and singed his smile, these— and their progeny—remain.

When death comes to someone we love, there is no consolation for the deep, immediate pain we feel. In the hours of final parting, the tears and the numbness to which our feelings guide us are the kindest elements of our own humanity. They open our emptiness and our sense of loss; and, as rain prepares the earth for growth, they tender our spirit, so that healing may begin. When tears come, we must not withhold them: social constraints have no business here. With our mourning we honor the one we have loved and clearly understand how deeply they have graced our lives.

It is only with the passage of time that our days will seem to acquire a wholeness again. For memory is partnered to time, and with it we may recall the joy we knew together. In this way we come to know that the one we have loved will always be with us. And, through memory, too, I believe we are finally moved to gratitude, for these pictures in the mind and heart allow us to see how insubstantial our lives might have been, if we had never had the opportunity to know and to love this person.

If we never love, we never have to mourn. But, if we never love, can it ever be said that we have lived?

Those who have opened their hearts to us have given us an infintely precious gift. For once love has been born, no power in heaven or on earth can ever truly take it away.

Sometimes I feel there is so much I have yet to do that I begin to fear I will run out of time before I have given my best to life.

In that anxiety I have found that it is necessary for me to pause and consider the good things I might have already done. Only in those moments of reflection do I clearly see that nothing of quality can ever be rushed. Neither art, nor love, nor life itself can be rendered with excellence when we watch the clock. Refinement requires time and care: there can be no substitute for these.

I will leave this earth knowing that I did not do all I had to do. But I hope that whatever I leave behind will say I cared; that its quality was not compromised; that I gave it my best; and that, occasionally, my best was enough to give a bit of life the honor it was due.

For—in the end—it is better to run out of time than to run out of the desire to continue to work and to live.

THE PROMISE

Nearly all human endeavors must yield to the flow of time.
Only love transcends it and allows us to merge
with that which is immortal.
With faith and perserverence, the promise is forever.

Across the years
I will walk with you —
in deep, green forests;
on shores of sand:
and when our time
on earth is through
in heaven, too,
you will have
my hand.

That a gesture as simple as the act of holding hands can speak so eloquently of the love two people share attests to the power within these extensions of the human heart.

Our hands express both the dignity of our individuality and the intensity of our aspiration to be joined with the world. More certainly than our voices, they tell of our devotion to our dreams; they signal our resistance to evil; they underscore our commitment to excellence in the work and activities to which we give our time and care.

Through their dexterity, that which we wish to accomplish in life may be brought to fruition, and each of us may contribute a uniquely personal gift to the world we share.

Physicians and dancers; farmers and teachers; watchmakers, carpenters, weavers and scribes: each of these and all of us employ the precision and delicacy which our hands allow. Guided by designs of our own determination, we move them to re-create the materials of our environment. And more often than we know, the products of our endeavors bring profoundly beneficial changes to the lives of those around us.

On an even more personal level, our hands are partnered to the sense of touch, and this allows us to communicate the most tender and intimate of our feelings. Even when words cannot tell the depth of our sorrow or our joy, our hands contain the measure of our emotion. Silently they speak of the presence of our love, while tending to the comfort of those for whom we deeply care. Their touch can be infinitely reassuring: their warmth can fill the deepest need.

One might travel the world in search of wonder, but the source of its surest manifestation is at our fingertips. Our hands are our birthright; and if we use them with wisdom, we may grace the world with wonders of our own.

Not long ago the members of my family gathered together that we might spend the Christmas holidays with one another. Between us, we travelled more than eight-thousand miles to make this possible. It had been several years since our last gathering, for our lives have carried us to distant and separate places. But this year each of us must have sensed the same yearning, for individually we decided to return to the company of our kin.

The shore towns of southern New Jersey were brittle with ice and day-old snow when I arrived. Within my parents' house, however, there was only the ease and warmth of people whose origins are intertwined and dearly-remembered. We spoke of our lives now with no pretense, celebrating each of our successes with immodest gladness, for instinctively we knew the difficulty with which these had come. We spoke, too, of our trials and disappointments, and—in turn—we rallied to one anothers' support: counseling; consoling; reassuring each of our own vulnerable spirits of the others' confidence and faith in its ability to rise, to shine, to come through at the end with flying colors.

My Dad showed movies of Mary Ellen, Peter, Tom and I in the long-ago moments of our early years. We laughed at the squinting babies, rambunctious toddlers, knock-kneed and cow-licked summer children, for they were us; and in those fleeting, flashing images we found early evidence of the peculiarities which have given each of us our individual and undeniable character.

We were gentler to one another as we gathered around my Mom's Christmas turkey and the table she had spread to its edges with the steaming bowls of her own handiwork. And, later still, we were quiet and almost melan-choloy in the smiles we gave to one another, as we exchanged gifts beneath the bright lights of the tree.

And it was not until the very end, in parting again, that the word "love" was ever mentioned. Even then, it was almost lost in the robust good cheer we extended to the door, to the porch, to the driveway and to our separate cars, as we passed slowly, waving, into the night.

Among those who carry it so surely within them, perhaps the word itself is of little consequence. But that which it represents—the continuity of trust, tenderness and infinite affection—displaces any other consequence to which we may give the moments of our lives. And certainly no other word can stir people from the comfort and security of their own settlements and carry them gladly back through the harshness of winter to share so few hours of such simple pleasure.

Through the glazed glass of my car window as I moved away from my parents' house on Christmas Eve, I saw my mother, lifting her hand and calling to me across the frozen lawn. I could not hear her voice. But, as she stood smiling within that frame of colored lights, I knew what she was saying. And with outstretched fingers I caught her love and—in frosty breaths of midnight air—sent back the fullness of my own.

The rain has stopped.

The cups before us are empty.
On the street outside the cafe, some of the cars have their headlights on,
for the shadows of dusk have already fallen on Sausalito.
On the sidewalk there are more people now: men and women, heading
home. A few of them have entered the cafe for a drink. They sit quietly, alone
or in pairs; tired, perhaps; or merely muted by the long grayness of the day.
An old woman enters, selling flowers. She finds no customers, until a
young man at a table near the back of the room buys a red rose for the young
woman at his side. The flower-seller smiles, satisfied. She moves to the door
and passes into the deepening dusk.
The window beside us is still flecked with rain. As we look through it, the
lights from the street turn these drops into briefly-shining miniature stars. But
more lovely than this is the far-off silhouette of the city of San Francisco. Out
of our sight, beyond the Golden Gate, the sun has again come through the
clouds; and in its setting it has cast a rosey hue upon the western face of the
city. Softly it glows, glistening with the sheen of a million pin-point lights,
drawing a line of human celebration between the somber Bay and sky.
Witnessing this, I again know why I have chosen to live here. Few other
places I have known contain such abundant magic; no other so readily inspires
that same quality in the lives of those who dwell within its light.

Across the table I look at you, wondering if you have felt it, too; wondering if it will bring you back.

Your eyes remain fixed on the glass. You breathe deeply, as if content; and the lines of your mouth are so slightly turned that you might be smiling.

I hope that you are.

We talk a little longer, but soon the ferry comes into view. Its foghorn signals, groaning deeply, like a great bear rising from its winter sleep.

You must return to the city.

I will remain in Sausalito and take the last ferry back, but I will walk with you to the landing.

We gather our things together and leave the now-familiar warmth of the cafe. In the square of light out front, we stand for a moment gazing back, as people always seem to do. Then we turn and move into the night.

At the ferry ramp we give our hands again; and I am secretly pleased that you are as awkward in parting as I. We thank each other and say the usual things our language has provided for such moments. Then, exchanging nods and smiles, we move apart; and I watch as you descend the ramp and pass into the bright interior of the small ship.

I remain at the dock, gazing at the ferry and then at the stars that have begun to break through the clouds above. Moments later I see you at the rail of the upper deck; and as the foghorn blasts its throaty note, you shortly lift your hand.

As the boat begins to move out upon the Bay, I fumble for words to call to you. I cannot say good-bye; each of us has heard that too often. Its finality stings and severs hope.

Then, as the boat turns upon the churning water, and you move further away, I finally recall the timeless chant, extended to voyagers on every sea. Through cupped hands I call "Godspeed" to you.

A single word, perhaps unheard, but meant to carry so many more.

Darkness has enveloped the ferry. I cannot see you now. But if you can still distinguish the small, solitary figure of a man upon the dock, know that this is what he intended to say:

May all your travels bring you peace.
May each new journey unfurl your heart.

The text of this book is set in ten point Sabon with italic.
The pages beside each drawing are typeset in twelve point Kentonian.

This work was produced at the West Coast Print Center, Berkeley, California.